WILLIAMS, M.   WS

Joseph and his magnificent coat of
many colours.

957   Pbk

THIS WALKER BOOK BELONGS TO:

_____

_____

_____

_____

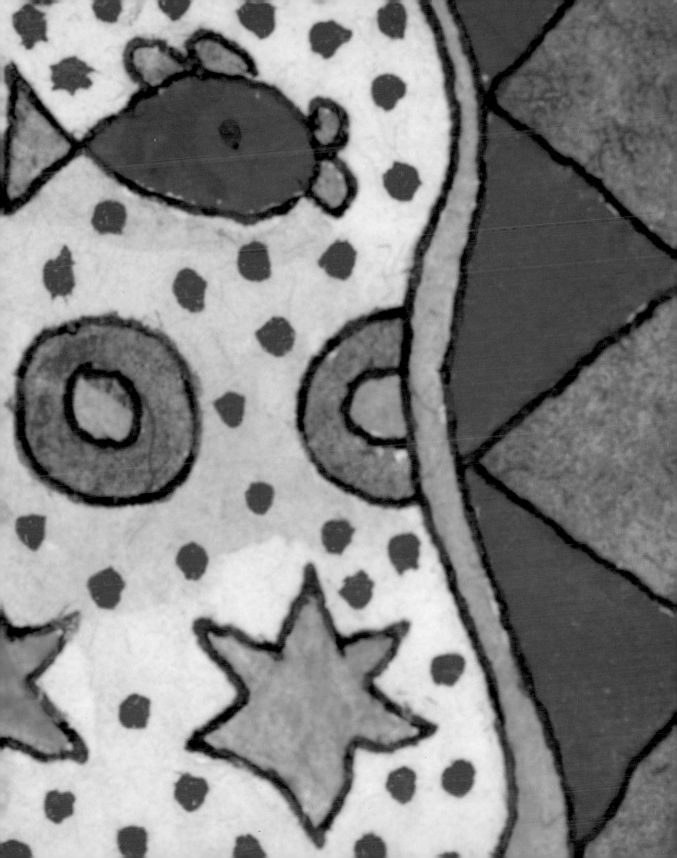

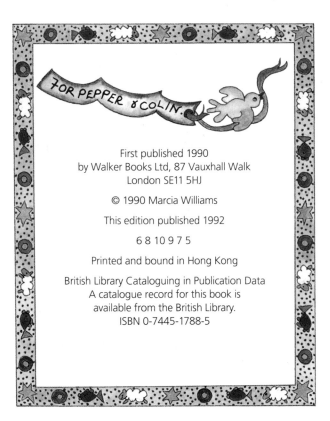

FOR PEPPER & COLIN.

First published 1990
by Walker Books Ltd, 87 Vauxhall Walk
London SE11 5HJ

© 1990 Marcia Williams

This edition published 1992

6 8 10 9 7 5

Printed and bound in Hong Kong

British Library Cataloguing in Publication Data
A catalogue record for this book is
available from the British Library.
ISBN 0-7445-1788-5

JOSEPH
and his
MAGNIFICENT COAT
OF MANY COLOURS

Written and illustrated by
Marcia Williams

WALKER BOOKS
AND SUBSIDIARIES
LONDON • BOSTON • SYDNEY

There once lived, in the land of Canaan,

a farmer called Jacob.

Jacob had twelve fine sons,

but the one he loved best was Joseph.

HAPPY 17th BIRTHDAY

Jacob gave Joseph a magnificent coat of many colours,

In Joseph's first dream,

he and his brothers were binding corn.

In this dream, Joseph's sheaf rose and stood upright

and his brothers' sheaves bowed down before it.

In Joseph's second dream

the sun, the moon and eleven stars

bowed down before him as though he were king.

Joseph's father believed the dreams meant

We must not forget these dreams.

that Joseph would become a great ruler.

But one of the brothers, named Reuben,

persuaded the others not to kill Joseph.

Instead, they stripped off his magnificent coat

and cast him into a pit.

Then, at midday, as the brothers sat down to eat,

they saw a company of Ishmaelites ride over the hill,

their camels loaded with spices to sell in Egypt.

The brothers decided to sell Joseph to the travellers

in exchange for a bag of silver.

Then they dipped Joseph's beautiful coat in blood,

and returned home to their father.

Jacob was heartbroken when he saw the coat.

Believing that Joseph had been killed by wild beasts,

he put on sackcloth and mourned his favourite son.

For two years Joseph languished in prison.

The other prisoners liked and respected him,

for he was a wise interpreter of their dreams.

But for Joseph it was a sad and lonely time.

sat puzzling over two strange dreams.

His wise man could not fathom their meaning,

so Joseph was brought out of prison

and asked to interpret them.

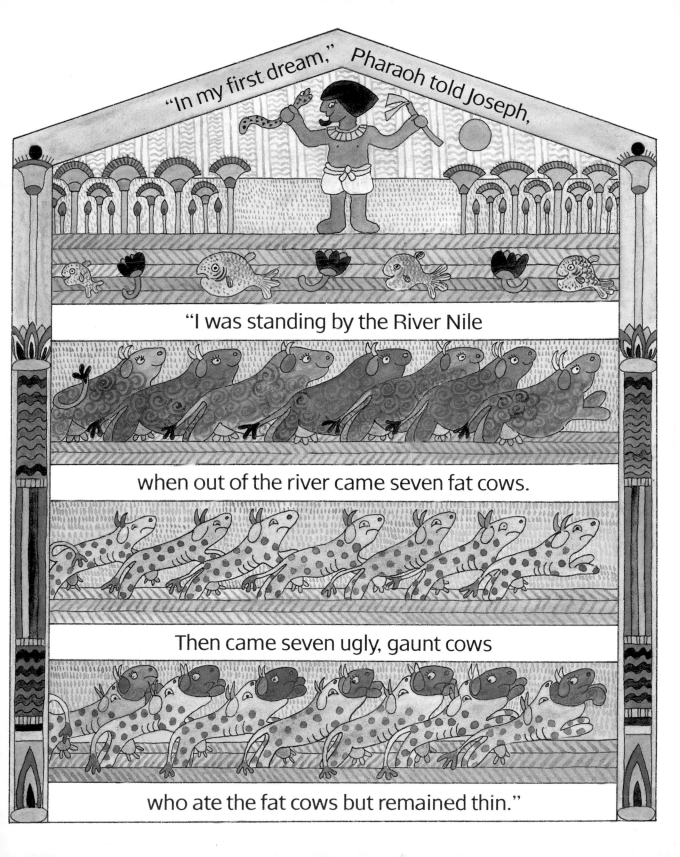

Joseph pretended to think his brothers were spies,

for he wished to see if they were still evil.

He threatened to enslave Benjamin, the youngest.

His brothers were distraught —

losing Benjamin would break their father's heart.

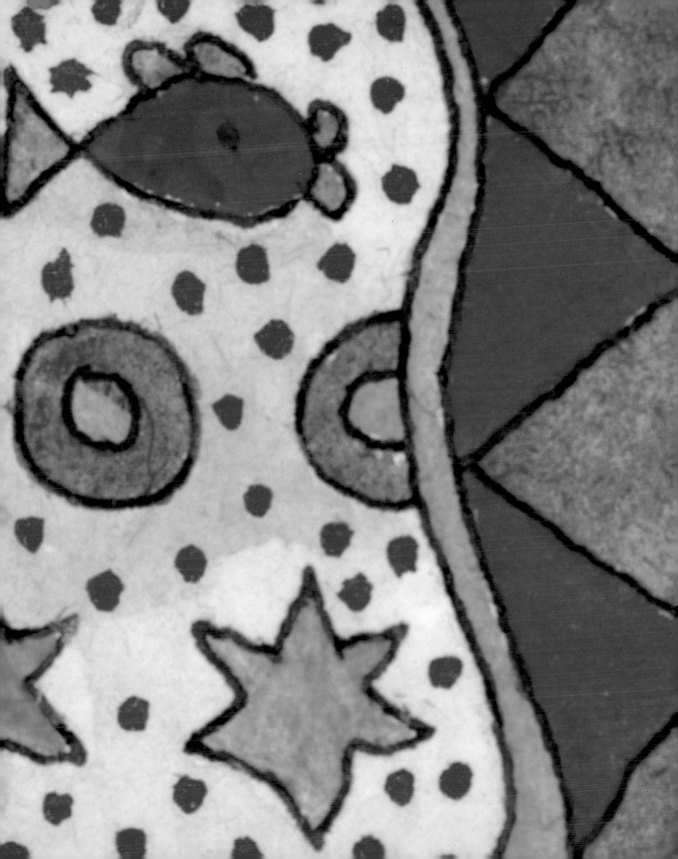

MORE WALKER PAPERBACKS
For You to Enjoy

Also by Marcia Williams

THE AMAZING STORY OF NOAH'S ARK

"Friendly, lively and intricate… Beautifully coloured borders." *The Observer*

"Commendably close to the original." *The Junior Bookshelf*

0-7445-1469-X   £3.99

JONAH AND THE WHALE

One of the most dramatic and colourful of all Old Testament stories brought vividly to life.

"The decorative pages are very well designed and prettily coloured."
Raymond Briggs, The Times Educational Supplement

0-7445-1735-4   £3.99

WHEN I WAS LITTLE

A series of intriguing comparisons between life now and what it was like, according to granny, in her day.

"Delightful… Bright, detailed illustrations provide 2-7 year olds with lots to look at and smile about, and the words are both simple and charming."
Practical Parenting

0-7445-1765-6   £3.99